Blackbeard's Last Stand

Alan MacDonald

Illustrated by Brian Lee

OXFORD
UNIVERSITY PRESS

OXFORD

UNIVERSITY PRESS

Great Clarendon Street, Oxford OX2 6DP

Oxford University Press is a department of the University of Oxford.
It furthers the University's objective of excellence in research, scholarship,
and education by publishing worldwide in

Oxford New York

Auckland Bangkok Buenos Aires Cape Town Chennai
Dar es Salaam Delhi Hong Kong Istanbul Karachi Kolkata
Kuala Lumpur Madrid Melbourne Mexico City Mumbai Nairobi
São Paulo Shanghai Taipei Tokyo Toronto

Oxford is a registered trade mark of Oxford University Press
in the UK and in certain other countries

British Library Cataloguing in Publication Data

Data available

ISBN 0 19 919 643 5

3 5 7 9 10 8 6 4

Mixed Pack (1 of 6 different titles): ISBN 0 19 919647 8
Class Pack (6 copies of 6 titles): ISBN 0 19 919646 X

Illustrated by Brian Lee

Acknowledgements
p4 Bettmann/Corbis UK Ltd.; p4 Hulton|Archive/Getty Images;
pp4/5 Hulton|Archive/Getty Images; p7 Hulton|Archive/Getty
Images; p16 North Carolina Maritime Museum; p17 Christie's
Images/Corbis UK Ltd.; p23 AKG – London; p27 North Carolina
Maritime Museum; p44 Bettmann/Corbis UK Ltd.; p45 Ronald
Grant Archive; p46 Bettmann/Corbis UK Ltd.; pp46/47 Corel;
p47 Corbis UK Ltd.

Printed in China

Contents

Introduction

The legend of Blackbeard is based on historical fact. He was at the height of his fame between 1716 and 1718. So, in just two short years, one man became the most famous pirate of all time!

During the 18th century pirates sailed the seas, attacking and robbing ships to make their fortune.

Pirate battle, around 1650.
The pirate ship is flying a pirate
flag and is attracting another ship

Blackbeard was a real-life man called Edward Drummond or Teach.

This nickname and the man himself were feared all along the east coast of America. He was huge and struck fear into the hearts of his victims. Others were daring, but Blackbeard was a madman who was afraid of nothing. He was as cruel to his own crew as to his enemies.

The Governor of Virginia begged the British Navy to help. He must be stopped or no ship would ever be safe!

This is the story of Blackbeard's Last Stand.

This picture shows the ideal pirate, holding the blade of a dagger in his mouth. A pirate ship is also shown

He's Pure Evil

Blackbeard – the name made my blood run cold. I read the letter for the third time, hoping there was some mistake. But there was no mistake. It was addressed to me – **Lieutenant** Robert Maynard – and my orders were clear. I was to hunt down the pirate Blackbeard and bring him back, dead or alive.

Don't think I'm a coward. I'd spent half my life in the Royal Navy. And I'd fought in more battles than I can remember. Pirates don't scare me. But I'd never faced anyone like Blackbeard. He wasn't just another pirate. He was a monster, a fire-breathing madman.

Blackbeard's name was known far and wide in America. Some people said he was the devil himself. And no wonder they were scared. No one was safe from Blackbeard. He sailed off the coast of Carolina, robbing every ship he set eyes on.

Blackbeard, around 1715. Note the flaming brands in his hair

When a captain heard it was Blackbeard, he often gave in without a fight. It was safer to surrender. That way you might escape with your life.

I'd never seen Blackbeard for myself, but of course I'd heard all the tales. They said Blackbeard was a giant of a man – more than two metres tall. His dark beard covered half his face. In battle he carried six loaded **pistols** and a sword as heavy as a shovel. No wonder his enemies were terrified.

There were many stories about Blackbeard's cruel games. His favourite one was playing with fire. "Come on you dogs!" he would roar. "Let's make a hell of our own and see who can last the longest." His pirates would follow him down into the hold – the dark space under the deck. No one dared to disobey their captain.

Then Blackbeard would light fires in that dark place. Soon the **hold** would be filled with choking, black smoke. One by one the pirates would rush up the ladder to escape. Their eyes watered and they gasped for fresh air. The last one to give in was always their captain. He would come on deck roaring with laughter. Once again he'd proved that no man was a match for Blackbeard.

This was the madman they were sending me to catch. I don't mind admitting that I was scared. If Blackbeard didn't scare you, then you were either a fool or a liar.

I reached for my hat and left my cabin. I had called the crew together and they were all waiting for me up on deck.

Some of the crew had
sailed with me for seven years or more.
And now I had to tell them. I took out
the letter from my pocket and read it
out loud. When I spoke the name of
Blackbeard, a gasp escaped from the
crew. I kept reading as if I hadn't
noticed. But when I finished, they were
staring at me as if I'd gone mad.

"That will be all," I said. "We sail at dawn."

There was a murmur. Munro, the first mate, was pushed to the front.

"Beg your pardon sir, but the men have asked me to speak. They don't like the sound of this."

"Don't like it?" I said. "You're in the navy! You're not paid to like it."

"But Blackbeard, sir, he's pure evil," said Munro. He looked round at the others.

They all nodded and started to speak at once. "It's true," said one. "I heard he shot one of his own men."

"That's right. Shot him in the leg. For nothing at all. Just to teach his men a lesson."

"He breathes fire."

"He puts matches in his hair. Lighted matches."

I waited until they'd finished. Then I folded my arms. "So you're all scared, are you?" I asked.

"We're not scared of any man," replied Munro. "But Blackbeard's not a man. He's a devil."

I laughed out loud. "You've been listening to too many stories!

Blackbeard is a pirate and my orders are to hunt him down. Now we've wasted enough time. Get this ship ready to sail."

The crew began to move away, grumbling in low voices. As I turned my back I heard someone say, "You'll never kill him, remember that."

Ocracoke Inlet

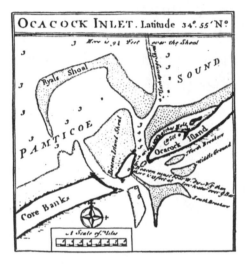

Old map of Ocracoke Inlet (North Carolina)

Blackbeard's ship was called the *Adventure*. Our spies told us it was sitting in a bay called Ocracoke Inlet. The bay was too shallow for a large navy ship. That meant I'd have to attack Blackbeard with small boats called **sloops**.

A sloop was small and fast, but ours didn't have any cannons. Blackbeard's ship was armed with 40 big guns. And that was what worried me most. One shot from those cannons could send our two sloops to the bottom of the sea.

By evening the next day we came in sight of the bay.

There was the *Adventure*, just as we'd been told, at anchor. Blackbeard was taking on board food and water.

A sloop like the ones Maynard was in charge of

Munro came and stood beside me. "That's him all right. What do we do, sir? Attack them now?"

"Not yet," I said. "We'll wait till morning. If he wants to run, he'll have to get past us first."

"Oh, he won't run away," said Munro. "Not if I know that devil. Not him, sir."

He spat over the side and turned away.

I gave orders to anchor our boats near

the mouth of the bay. Night fell, and we
sat down to wait. On my boat I had 35
men. The rest of my men were in the
other boat with one of my best officers,
Baker.

If there was going to be a battle I
guessed that we outnumbered the
pirates. But that didn't make me feel
any better. Blackbeard had his mighty
cannons. They were the danger.

I was worried about my men too. Ever since I'd told them our orders, I'd noticed a change. Some of them had become restless and silent. Sometimes, I caught them whispering to each other. They believed that going after Blackbeard was madness. That I was leading them to certain death.

Secretly, I wondered if they were right. If I could have turned back I would have. But I was a captain in the Royal Navy and I had to obey orders. It was far too late for turning back.

Blackbeard's Flag

The waiting didn't help our nerves. All
night we sat on our boats. The wind
sang in the rigging. Every creak and
groan of the ship made me reach for my
pistol. I drifted off to sleep. I dreamed
that pirates were swarming all over my
ship. I saw Blackbeard's great bearded
face looking down on me. He raised his
sword – and I woke up in a cold sweat.

There was someone knocking at my cabin door.

It was Munro, the first mate.

"Sorry to wake you, sir, but come up and listen to this."

I went up on deck. Sounds drifted across the water on the wind. Shouts and laughter were coming from the pirates' ship. Some of them began to sing noisily and other voices joined in.

"Drunk!" Munro snorted in disgust. "And they've been like that since midnight."

Five extendable telescopes from the period

"Let them drink," I replied. "They won't be so cheerful when they see us."

Dawn broke. It was a gloomy morning. A cold mist had rolled in from the sea.

Munro stood with me on deck.

I passed him my **telescope** and he turned it on the *Adventure*. "I can't see anything, sir," he said. "The mist is too thick. Do we wait for them to make a move?"

"No," I replied. "Let's go and wake them up. They've slept for long enough."

I'd had enough of waiting. My men would feel better when they had some action. Besides I wanted to give Blackbeard a surprise.

Together our two boats swam through the gloom towards the pirates' ship. The mist folded around us like a white blanket.

Suddenly the pirates' ship loomed out of the mist. We were close enough to see people moving about on deck. The pirates were getting to their feet and rubbing their eyes.

One of them came to the side of the ship to stare at us. He towered over the rest like a giant. His beard cast a dark shadow across his face. It was Blackbeard himself!

"Villains! Who are you?" he roared at us.

I pointed to our **mast** where the British flag was flying.

"You can see from our flag we are not pirates," I called back.

"Send a boat, then," roared Blackbeard. "Come aboard, so I can see who you are."

"I can't spare a boat," I called back. "But when I come I'll be bringing my pistols."

My men laughed at this threat. But my words sent Blackbeard into a rage. He shook his sword at us and shouted curses. "Come on, then! You'll be sorry you ever set eyes on me!"

He shouted an order to his men and they ran up their own flag. It wasn't the usual pirate **skull and cross bones**. Blackbeard's flag showed a skeleton pointing a spear at a blood red heart. We all knew what it meant. Death to the pirates' enemies.

Big Guns

Seconds later, I realised the *Adventure* was moving. The pirates had cut their ropes and were sliding away fast towards the sea. If we didn't act quickly, they would get away.

Baker's boat was ahead of mine and he steered it to block their escape. The *Adventure* changed course to avoid a crash. On deck, I could see men running about. Blackbeard was giving the orders and the pirates were loading their cannons.

A few seconds later, the first of the big guns boomed. There was a splash in the sea ahead of us.

Another boom.
Then I saw that Baker's
ship was hit. The largest sail was on fire.
A moment later the mast toppled down
on to the deck with a mighty crash.
Without its sail, the boat would drift
helplessly.

In two shots Blackbeard's cannons had destroyed one of my boats. Now I would have to fight him on my own.

"They're getting away!" Munro shouted beside me. "The wind has dropped."

I looked up. Sure enough, our sails were drooping. "Pull on the oars!" I ordered. "Every man to his post."

Soon we were gaining on the *Adventure* again. Without the wind in their sails, the pirates couldn't get away.

But Blackbeard wasn't trying to escape. He was more than ready to stand and fight. As soon as we were close, I knew his cannons would be pointing at us.

"Keep rowing! We're catching them!" I shouted. It was true. The gap was closing between us and the *Adventure*. I ordered my crew to leave their oars. Now it was our turn to fire back.

We kept up a steady fire on the pirates
with our **rifles**. But they might as well
have been **pea-shooters**. I watched
helplessly as the pirates loaded their
great cannons again. Any moment now
they would open fire on us.

There was a puff of smoke and the first shot whistled over our heads, making me duck. We weren't so lucky with the next one. I heard a crash behind me and screams of pain. At least four of my men lay on the deck and others were trying to put out the flames.

A moment later, a third cannonball shook our boat .

Munro was at my side, shouting in my ear. "It's no use, sir. We're an easy target! If we don't pull back they'll blow us all to pieces!"

"And let them get away?" I shouted. "Not while I'm giving the orders. Tell the men to get below decks."

"What about you?" Munro asked.

"You heard me! Get them all below!" I roared back.

As I spoke there were more cries behind me. Men started to pick up the wounded and carry them into the hold. I counted them as they went down the ladder. I guessed I had thirteen men left. All the rest were dead or wounded.

"Stay below until I give the order," I said as I closed the hatch.

Now there were only two of us left on deck. Myself and Sharp who was steering the boat.

If Blackbeard wanted to run, I wouldn't be able to stop him. But I was counting on his love of a battle. The prize of capturing a navy ship would be far too good to miss.

Sure enough, I could see the *Adventure* was steering closer to us. Blackbeard was coming in for the kill.

Suddenly the big guns stopped booming. For a moment there was silence. Then something exploded near my head, so that I had to dive behind a barrel. It wasn't a cannonball. The pirates were showering us with bottle **hand grenades**. I crouched down while the deadly missiles rained down all around me.

When I looked again the air was filled with smoke. Through it, I could just see the towering figure of Blackbeard on the deck of the *Adventure*.

He waved a pistol and shouted to his men, "Follow me boys! There's only three or four of them still standing. Let's climb aboard and cut them to pieces!"

The Trap

Blackbeard was the first to board our ship. Next came a dozen pirates, swarming after him like an army of rats. This was exactly what I'd been waiting for. Blackbeard had walked right into my trap.

I pulled open the hatch and shouted down to my men, "Now! Up on deck! Every man who can hold a sword!"

My crew came pouring up the ladder. When they saw that they'd been tricked, the pirates stopped in their tracks. They'd expected to find a ship at their mercy. Instead, they were faced with thirteen sailors armed with swords and rifles.

Blackbeard only paused for a second. If it was going to be a battle, he was ready.

Up close, he was even more terrible
than I'd imagined. His thick beard was
as black as coal. Smoke curled round his
head from burning matches in his hair.
He had a pistol in one hand and his
huge sword in the other. As he waded
forward he roared like an angry bear.

With the first swing of his sword, one of my men fell dead to the ground. The next moment, I found myself face to face with the giant himself. He aimed a pistol at me and I fired back.

Luckily, my shot hit him in the shoulder and I saw him stagger back. But the wound didn't stop him. It only made him wilder than ever. Howling with rage, he came storming forward again.

Before I had time to reload, he was on top of me. His huge sword came sweeping down. I raised my sword to take the blow – but it snapped in half like a twig. Now the giant had me at his mercy. I fumbled with my pistol but it was too late. Blackbeard showed his teeth in a grin and raised his sword again...

The blow never came. From somewhere Munro jumped in front of me. I saw him thrust his sword at the pirate king. Blackbeard staggered back. Three or four of my men surrounded him. Still he came forward, slashing with his great sword left and right.

I reloaded my pistols and fired at him once, twice. Blackbeard stood for a moment, his eyes bulging like a toad. Then he toppled forward on to the deck.

An illustration showing Blackbeard and Maynard duelling

With their captain dead, the pirates knew they were beaten. Before long they had all surrendered and put down their weapons. I had them all put in chains and locked up below deck.

As for Blackbeard – his last stand had been a terrible one but now it was over. The monster lay dead on the deck.

"You see, he was just a pirate," I told Munro as we sailed for home. "All this talk of it being impossible to kill him was nonsense."

"All the same," replied Munro. "I'll be glad when he's off this boat and buried under the ground."

I leaned on the rail and looked out to sea. Maybe Munro was right in a way. Blackbeard was dead. But I had a feeling that his name would live on for as long as stories of pirates were told.

Poster for the 1952 film
Blackbeard the Pirate

Story Background

Did you know that Blackbeard was the inspiration for the character of Long John Silver in Robert Louis Stevenson's *Treasure Island*?

His real name was Edward Drummond, later Teach (although there are different spellings of this). He came from Bristol. He was probably from a good educated family as he could read and write.

Captain Kidd, another famous pirate, finishes off an opponent with a bucket!

Did you know that there were also female pirates on the High Seas? Born in London, Mary Read was raised as a boy. She later dressed as a man and became a pirate. She met Ann Bonney, another female pirate, aboard a pirate ship and they became close friends. They both married other pirates, but they lived and fought like the toughest men – even when they were both pregnant!

Mary Read and Ann Bonney were tough female pirates

Index

Glossary

hand grenades small explosive shells thrown by hand

hold a cavity in the ship below deck where cargo is kept

Lieutenant navy officer just below the rank of Lieutenant-Commander

mast a long main pole of iron or timber set up to support the sails

pea-shooter a toy tube from which dried peas are shot by blowing

pistol a small firearm held and fired by one hand

rifles guns, with long barrels, fired from the shoulder

skull and cross bones a flag showing a bare skull with two thigh bones crossed below it as a symbol of piracy or death. Traditionally flown by pirates

sloop a small one-masted vessel with a mainsail and small triangular sail

telescope an optical instrument using mirrors to make faraway objects look larger and nearer